I Have Crossed An Ocean

I Have Crossed An Ocean

EDITED BY

JONATHAN MORLEY

Heaventree

I Have Crossed An Ocean

First edition 2004
© Heaventree Press 2004

Selection and Introduction © Heaventree Press
Copyright of individual contributions remains with the authors.
ISBN 0-9545317-5-2

Heaventree logo design by Panna Chauhan
Printed by Cromwell Ltd, Trowbridge, Wiltshire

Published by

The Heaventree Press
PO Box 3342
Coventry
CV1 5YB
England

Contents

Introduction

Coventry is home to immigrant communities from all over the world. This book began with the recognition that such arrivals can have a profound and beneficial effect on the multicultural melting pot of these isles, even this far inland, and that working collaboratively to record something of their trials and achievements in the city could be an appropriate project for Heaventree, a local small press.

Funding was applied for to run a series of writing workshops for refugees and minority groups, and publish *I Have Crossed An Ocean* for free distribution. Photographers included, we have worked with refugees from Bosnia, Pakistan, Iran, Iraq, Kurdistan, Togo, Morocco, Kenya, Somalia, Sudan, Congo and Zimbabwe; most are represented in the book. To this list were added the contributions of resident foreign workers and international students. In this (the most random) group are people from Australia, Romania, Italy, Botswana, Jamaica, Columbia, Canada and the USA. Finally it was decided that some local writers, black, white and Asian, could be included if their work contained themes relevant to the anthology; provision for immigrants need not equate to a neglect of their host communities. Beyond this, no editorial indication is given as to place of origin. These writers are people, and nothing more. By confusing the demographic in this way I hope to assert that the ideas, argument and aesthetic of a text are open to all, and writers should go first on these things and only when forced by the presence of inequality take positions on race, ethnicity and cultural differences, those giant facts whose existence will never, need never, be challenged. All translations were made collaboratively between author and editor, except those by Alberto Orengo, Letizia Gramaglia and Kala Grant, provided by the authors, and the poems from the Urdu of Ali Ahmed, adapted from earlier versions by M. A. Qureshi.

This brings us to the question, is there an aesthetic at work in this collection? For me, the most disturbing passages are not to be found in the chilling avant-gardism of Adrian Urmanov, in the issue-led riddims of Kim Trusty and Kala Grant, or in Roy Pargetter's portrayal of urban deprivation, brilliant as these are, but in the collection of poems, songs and stories produced by the Coventry Refugee Centre's Jigsaw group (pages 50-59). It is sobering to read the work of these youngsters, aged between 9 and 14, with their images of murder, suicide, sleeplessness and loss. That all is not totally bleak and hopeless is a tribute to George Ttoouli, who led those workshops and transcribed the poems. I find myself, no Fanon, balking at a psychological interpretation: those poor kids didn't really undergo this stuff, did they? Maybe they just saw it in films or computer games? Cultural relativism: we don't even see our inability to comprehend real horror as a luxury, here in the decadent 'West'. The core experience for refugees is a strange and, to most British people, unimaginable mixture of hurt, anger, poverty, fear, worry, linguistic difficulty, nightmarish journeys, social alienation, Kafkaesque bureaucracy, looming home office judgments, official secrecy, misinformation and inefficiency, and extremes of protest and opinion on all sides: in a word, of uncertainty. At its most powerful, the politicisation forced by this context can offer some fascinating readings. Kurdistan, for example, no longer has a recorded history—its architecture and literature have been systematically destroyed by Iraqi, Iranian, Syrian and Turkish occupation—so a Kurdish poem about Kenilworth Castle's ancient stones and stories may have a far deeper thematic resonance than a stylistic approximation in English by a lady from Kenilworth. Similarly the debates on impersonality, currently viewed as unfashionably intellectual by this country's major poetry publishers, are given a new vitality by refugees: why on earth should someone who has seen their family murdered before their eyes want to write about their personal feelings? One writer told me (this is not included in the collection): "My heart is cold. It has never been warm for one minute. If my heart remains cold all my life, it would be better that I had died." The possibility that this statement was not made for literary effect but is true makes a mockery of certain post-Romantic poetics and their focus on the irresistible charms of darkness, despair and evil. Conversely, the new cynics might want to think again about the uses of escapism in this context (though Wallace Stevens' verse about the thin men of Haddam who laze about imagining golden birds and remain blind to the blackbirds scurrying at the women's feet took on wry overtones when read in the company of a Zimbabwean and a Somali woman...).

This book is, then, political, and the months spent organising and editing coincided with a local election campaign where I stood against the bigotry of the British

National Party in the company of a coalition of writers, musicians, care workers, students and Socialists. As a poet I could not stand by and let fascists spread their filth unchallenged. No doubt this will raise some hackles; a sad pattern developed among some writers and musicians whereby otherwise intelligent, highly motivated and critical thinkers could not bring themselves to support us by leafleting or even visiting the relevant council estate to take a look at the problems, let alone giving a performance or public statement against the fascists. 'We're not going to sing alongside Socialists,' they'd argue, or, more cerebrally, 'Art's subversive purity will be lost if it soils itself by engaging with temporal politics.' However clever they may be, the end result was to condemn our work in the same terms as the BNP had in the letters page of The Coventry Observer: saying racism is wrong is totalitarianism, apparently. I would argue that these people's failure to bring proper intellectual analysis to bear on the situation reflects unflatteringly their own artistic capabilities, if not the general counterculture. Mario Vargas Llosa has justified artistic engagement with politics on the grounds that the mediocrity of totalitarian culture is the mortal enemy of artistic expression, and few arguments are as mediocre as the pathetic semantic debates of the local BNP: 'well, what's a fascist anyway?' From empirical observation of their behaviour and study of the provincial ugly newsrags they produce, a fascist is one who imagines that his state, in this case Little Britain, floats like a fake jewel in the sea with no dependence on the usual international patterns of trade and international exchange; whose arguments are based on emotion rather than reason; whose perception never penetrates below the superficialities of skin colour, race and cultural difference and who defines himself always in terms of who he is not; who sends death threats to the manager of a local refugee football team; who brings Alsatian dogs to menace his electorate on the campaign trail and sets shaven-headed thugs on guard in the car park while his votes are being counted; whose ultimate goal is to live alone on a vast swathe of Lebensraum stretching on forever. A fascist in the year 2004 is—be he from the racist BNP or the xenophobic UKIP (personally I fail to see how hostility to people who look *similar* to you is any better than racism)—an ignorant, wrecking bully who craves, no matter what he may trumpet at election time, to spoil British democracy by dragging us backwards in time to the dark ages. It was good to see young people, despite the recent rightward shift nationwide, encouraged by these arguments to campaign and steal 200 votes from the BNP in the Tile Hill estate, their Coventry stronghold. The June 10th elections have been the dark crucible in which this book's processes of translation and creativity flare with brightness and urgency.

Our findings on the ground in Tile Hill have been that working people, angered beyond measure at a grossly unfair council tax, a systematic policy of privatisation and cuts in housing and social services, and an arrogant and aloof government of warmongering hypocrites, turn to far-right extremism as a protest vote. "Yeah, I'm voting for the BNP, but I wouldn't want them to get in," one voter told us. "I don't want them in power, I'm not stupid." The presence on ballot papers of one vote each for the Liberal Democrats, the Socialist Party and the

BNP bore this out. But how can we argue that immigration (race + economics) is not the real issue when, across mainstream politics, our leaders queue up to declare their anti-immigration credentials? Take Coventry's MP, a stolid veteran of the car unions: 'I was the one who brought down the immigration minister,' says Bob Ainsworth. 'I was the one who got rid of the need for prima facie evidence in extradition cases,' says Bob Ainsworth. 'I was party chief whip when Labour lost control of my city council,' says Bob Ainsworth, a man destined for great things. The rational majority understand that fascists are ridiculous, and that democracy is safeguarded by precisely their right to argue their case with better opponents—this situation is weakened by those in government who, paranoid for power and duped by far-right rhetoric, will not admit what the links are between war, the importation of cheap, non-taxable labour into Britain, an excruciatingly slow system of case assessment for the right to stay and work legally, and the business lobby.

This lack of honesty makes mounting an argument against the BNP difficult. They have the right to stand, the establishment murmurs, and we cannot influence the electorate by urging people not to vote for them (the BNP themselves have no such qualms about the "old gang parties"). This caution then becomes exaggerated (and you have to ask yourself why) until any anti-racist or anti-fascist gesture is frowned upon as 'political'; so, for example, you have the ludicrous situation where representatives of the city's Multicultural Library Services are not allowed to speak out against racism in the local media (for The Coventry Telegraph's version of 'neutrality' see the Appendix on page 119). In case the so-called intelligentsia in government and the press still haven't grasped the point, allow me to spell it out: to refuse to address the real issues, to hide behind a constant jamboree of pop and porn, football and flag-waving, does not constitute political neutrality (nor a 'third way'), but rather acquiescence in a massive institutional shift to the right, and it is not far from this to the bland and choiceless folktale in which the fascists seek to consolidate their power. The centrist leadership have a *choice* to move leftwards if they so wish, by, for example, making strong positive statements about our need for immigration, by ceasing to do America's bidding in the Middle East, by pushing forward environmental policies that will help the Third World and by redistributing domestic wealth. Instead they *choose* to turn a blind eye to creeping fascism. We should not allow them to trick us into seeing their laziness as impartiality. I urge readers to explore positive, creative alternatives.

Many people have been involved in the writing of this book, and here I can only thank the principal figures. For core funding for the project I am indebted to the Millennium Commission's Campaign for Learning, and to Colin Bell of Frontline Audio Visual and Penny Walker of the Coventry Peace House, who helped secure funding and plan the workshops programme. Workers at the Coventry Refugee Centre, the Lula G Youth Group, Coventry West Indian Centre and the local Asian Literary Circle successfully coordinated various events. Liz Dembrowsky and Lindsey Holland took on many of the workshops, and Shruti Ravindran helped teach at short notice, as well as drawing a fantastic 'Refugee Boy' for publicity purposes. The photographs on pages 61 to 68 have been taken by refugee women as part of the 'Exiles' photography project, run in Coventry to a similar timescale by Alice Mahtani. Thanks to Alice and her funders, the Arts Council England, the Heart of England Fund and Coventry City Council, as well as to Colin Scott of the Positive Images Festival for ensuring the photos' inclusion in the book. The tireless advice and assistance of two very generous people at the University of Warwick, the novelist David Dabydeen and the poet David Morley, has been invaluable to my writing, editing and publishing. Heaventree could not do its poetic work locally without the support of Creative Coventry, particularly Clare Huby, Jo Whitford and Jane Howard. Finally, special mention must be made of my friend Richard Currie, without whose comradeship and good sense the anti-fascist campaign could not have operated. Rich has been immersed in work for his university finals, as well as on the waiting list for a major operation whose delay causes him physical pain, and his endurance, humour, determination and willingness to take on a just political cause in the teeth of difficult circumstances have been an inspiration. Big up to Melli, Lex and Rizzo, Kris, Henry 'Daddy Woody', George the Greekling and of course my long-suffering family. I hope you enjoy the book.

Jon Morley
Coventry, June 2004

from the Urdu of ALI AHMED

At the start of Love's journey

Hate's intensity has dimmed
the bright things of the world

black war hangs always
like a sword over our heads

the goblin hunger dances
in our deserted cities

our empty pots
ring like mouths of cannons.

They have stolen our fires
to forge their missiles

they have stolen our oil
to shine their boots

they peel our skin
for their flags of victory

they suck our blood
and spray their bullets red.

Love's journey leads us
through a minefield.

The wolves

Upstanding in expensive suits,
The wolves weep: how cheap is human blood!
They say we can vote out ignorance
And vote in bread and milk and honey.
They blindfold us with hope.
They tie stones to our stomachs,
As in autumn the coming winter
Invites the trees to drop their leaves for spring.
The wolves smash through the fences of our dreams
And claw off what remains of our flesh.
They say we need more wolves
To protect us from the wolves,
We poor sheep and goats.

MARTIN CVELBAR

Pigeons at home and away

He says I'm developing an unhealthy addiction to the teev. She looks up. There's gotta be something he says in mock despair and flicks around the five stations again. I don't know if I can take another home renovation show. So what if this twit in Stoke has a dingy hallway. I don't give a… The interior decorator says we need to open this up, let the light in. I'm going to the pub and he throws the remote into the darkest corner of the couch to nestle with the pens, chewy and 1p coins.

Coming? We won't know anyone there she says. Doesn't matter. Isn't there someplace else we could go? Umm, I don't think so. They don't have proper cafés here. And they were warmed by the thought of home and sitting under a jacaranda tree with friends and coffee. At least they have Sky there.

On the way to the pub, her nose began to run and dribbled onto her cerulean scarf. I forgot a hanky. He gesticulates where did they put the bloody sun? Can you remember when you saw it last? I can't. I like it she says wait till summer you'll like it then but I need a hanky. He hands her the remnant of a pulped and shredded tree. It is pale against the grey street and glows in the murk.

They walk around the Cathedral. It's incredible even if it's only a shell since the bomb hit I'm surprised anything's left standing she asks do you think its gothic? Umm, I don't know he says let's go to the medieval street. They walk past a newspaper vendor. Blair to cut asylum seekers in half. He says we're in but it looks like everyone else wants to come back too. Or maybe he's a magician. It's such a small island she says there's no space for them.

After a pint they step out of the crooked medieval freehouse and a woman walks towards them. She takes little pitter-patter steps and her whole body lurches forward then jerks back in a frenzied way. Her arms claw the air in front of her or flail to either side. It is a regal procession all her own. She has already elbowed one man aside so on the narrow footpath they stand to one side to let her pass. They are horrified but he feels as if he should doff his cap or at least help her. Her blue eyes are grim, her body out of control but her coiffed hair does not move. Down the street the kids playing between the Kingfisher Gallery and the church know her. They ridicule her. The woman impotently responds in her high falsetto voice and they laugh.

Let's go home she says but as they walk past a red brick pub he asks how about a quick one? She frowns but says alright. They push through the doors and immediately realise that everyone knows everyone else but they do not. They make their way quickly to a side booth and he asks her what she'd like. Someplace else. No this is ok he says it's warm. He goes to the bar and asks for a beer they don't have. Where's that accent from mate? Yorkshire. Ireland. Aussie? How ya goin' cobber? The barman grins from behind his handlebar moustache. Want some fush and chups? That's a New Zealander accent but yeah ok got some? Not today. Then what's that sign doing out front? It's Sunday.

He puts the pints on the table and tells her that they don't have any fish and chips today. No of course not she says what about the sign out front? He shrugs his shoulders and they watch the soccer. I didn't want any anyway she says. That's lucky he smiles. This is such a mad place she says.

There's a man at the bar, his belly distending his Arsenal shirt. He is the odd man out. He supports the Gunners who've just won. He's into another man's face with a finger. The other man is thin and responds by thumping his chest with his hands and crying c'mon c'mon and throwing a fist that splatters the fat man's stomach. He is up with a misguided pint glass and things explode as the crowd become involved. She is in shock and shouts let's get out of here... now! I haven't finished my pint but they head for the door. Fuck, fuck, fuck and he can see her hysteria. What were you doing? They'll be friends again in the morning no big deal. C'mon love and he takes her hand to reassure her. He takes her home.

The days did get longer and he reacquainted himself with the sun but he says it's so dark in here why do they make their windows so small? It's dark outside as well but you can turn on a light if you want besides it's warmer in winter. Maybe they don't like people looking inside? They were looking out their kitchen window with its panels of warped glass which gave odd reflections and distortions. Their backyard is sodden and empty apart from a shed in the corner and is loomed over by a council block of flats.

He wants to talk to her about the place they had come to. He asks d'you know what I saw today? Hang on what's that she says. In the dimness, a bird had fluttered to ground. It's a pigeon she says. It'll fly off in a moment he says but the bird pecks at the lawn instead. They watch in expectation but it nestles down. I'm going to take it some bread she says it looks tired. He is sceptical a tired pigeon? Try wholemeal.

She walks slowly towards the pigeon and he thinks it'll go now. He believes it has a sense of fear towards most humans. The bird cocks an eye at her. She rips the bread into small pieces and tosses it toward the pigeon that pecks it. She finds it a beautiful pigeon. It is slate blue with a ribbon around its neck and when the pigeon ruffles its plumage there is an iridescent swirl. She feeds the pigeon for a while then comes back in. I think it's a homing pigeon there's a tag on its leg. It'll probably go overnight he says you shouldn't feed it no doubt the owner would like it back but his tone isn't prohibitive. They both walk outside to feed the pigeon. They hold arms.

He is unable to sleep. He tosses and turns and then decides to go downstairs to watch some teev. Once there he goes to the kitchen but cannot see the pigeon in the dark. He goes back into the living room and flops into a recliner chair and raises the footrest. He turns on the plasma teev down low because he doesn't want to wake her up.

He flicks around the stations. He sees the end of in the line of fire and a show about black holes in space comes on. The narrator is talking about how nothing ever escapes from them, not even light, which is why we can't spot them with telescopes. They may even be in our very galaxy and we wouldn't know. But what if we stray too close to a supermassive black hole? We would be sucked into it and the planets would disintegrate one by one in a fiery apocalypse. As scientists cannot see black holes they are now looking for them by searching for the effects they have on what's around them.

They believe they have found a star being ripped apart by one and he now sees a long swirl of fire being dragged from the star into nothingness. But the more he looks at the teev he feels the opposite is happening. He believes that in the blackness there is a crack a rip in the fabric of space-time and he is standing on an imminent apocalypse. Just as he is beginning to feel very worried he looks up to find her sitting at the top of the stairs. The flickering light makes her face ashen. He asks what's up and she says it's almost dawn come back to bed.

She finds the phone number for the owner of the pigeon in Dover and he answers. No I don't want him back he's a flyaway. She says you've got to take him back he's your pigeon. Not anymore he replies he has to come back for that. But I don't want him. Look if you don't feed him he'll leave in a few days. I don't know if I can do that.

She hangs up and he walks in from work. You know the owner won't take his pigeon back? Well he's not much of a homing pigeon. We could always keep him she says. What if he says we take him down to the park chuck some bread about and bugger off? You know I think we need a drink to think this over. Or a think to drink this over. She grimaces at his joke.

At the pub she was saying that they even have pigeon couriers that would take the pigeon back to its owner but he wasn't interested. I don't think you can force him to take it back he says do you think other pigeon fanciers might be interested? They were at their local and one of the locals John had come over. He wasn't one of the finger in your face pint glass hurling pissing on your doorstep mob but rather liked talking about Rolf Harris, Men at Work and the Australian PM who touched up HRH. He tells them that he's never been to Australia but that he's thought about it. He'd like to. Now he was talking about sledging in cricket. She didn't like sport and she quickly tired of the conversation. She states we have a pigeon it flew in the other day and we don't know what to do with it. John quips you could take him down to the park throw some bread around and scarper. You know he said that too and they laugh.

She had asked do you want to go home now and he'd said but that's just it we can't can we? Besides I like it here but she says I'd rather be at home. So she'd left and he'd remained and now he wasn't in bed and it was almost daybreak. As the ambient light stole into the bedroom she began to get worried he would be late for work. Eventually she heard a rattle at the door and it was him. Where have you been she asked? Canley he replies. What the fuck were you doing in Canley? I don't know he says I must've been really drunk. What do you mean? I mean the last thing I really remember was talking to John about David Bowie and I said that's not how you say it in Australia you say Bowie and he said of course that's not what I'd say and then I wake up in the park at Canley with some kids pulling up saplings by their roots. Did you tell them not to? No I'm not mad.

He walks into the kitchen to get some breakfast and she tells him I'm going to call a man about converting the shed into a loft for the pigeon and he says alright but sure you don't want it to roam with the free range pigeons? I've got to take a shower what a night damn I wish I could remember it must've been good but I'm feeling a bit rough now.

She is recommended a man and she phones him. He talks about ventilating the shed, the nesting boxes and perches, the feeding hoppers that prevent the pigeon from fouling the grain and water containers but he says it depends on what you want to do with the pigeon are you going to race or breed it? If you want to race it you'll need to get a trap for the loft. When the pigeon comes back from the race you have to time it in and some fanciers use the widowhood method and keep their cocks separate from their hens so that they'll come back for their mate. They divide their loft between the two. She said no it's only for this pigeon.

It happens again. He'd been drinking with John again he could remember but that was it. He calls her on his mobile and she asks him where he is? I don't know. A man walks past and he asks hey mate where am I? He says I'm in Redditch and laughs. He gets home and says at least I'm seeing the country this way but she doesn't laugh. He's been hurt. He has a black eye and his ribs are bruised. Who did this she demands but he has no idea it was John wasn't it? Don't be bloody ridiculous. That guy she says has a real dark side. No you're wrong weirdly enough we're similar.

He doesn't go to work and mopes about the house getting over his hangover. Turning off the teev, he finds a holiday brochure from Exodus and idly flicks through it but then falls asleep. He dreams that he is running from something of absolute horror. He experiences the fear the living have when death pursues. He sees others standing still their bodies disintegrating. Other are being blown wildly apart while others have become mere shadows against walls. Finally he turns and sees the mushroom cloud he's been running from. He jolts awake in the late afternoon not knowing where he is but knowing the dream to be only a dream but of the worst kind.

She sits in the back garden sometimes going to the loft to see the pigeon. She goes inside the house for another cup of tea and finds him watching a place in the sun. He idly comments I wouldn't mind going there. That evening she puts her foot down and he doesn't go to the pub for his own good. She wants to talk to him about his drinking problem it's becoming an issue you should see someone about it. I don't want to go anyway he says I know when I've had enough. He watches one of his favourite movies the usual suspects then the news. He sees angry and bewildered people marching in London then a story about an earthquake in Turkey.

She learns how to hand feed the bird and she starts

gently to handle it by cupping it underneath its breast. She learns to spread the pigeon's wings to check for any malformations. She lets it out in the morning after he goes to work and watches it soar away. She cleans out the loft and then calls it back. It lands on the tin roof and scratches about like the rattling of keys before it enters the loft. Sometimes she sits in the loft and talks to the pigeon and it listens with its bright eyes and she stares out the loft's door at the house. Before he gets home from work she lets it out for another hour and watches it cartwheel past the council block.

He was down at the pub with John. He hadn't been out in the past fortnight since his last episode but he was tired of being cooped up in the house. They were talking about the Ashes although neither were sure when the next one would be. John said that they had pigeons in the outfield at the cricket in Australia. John remembers when one was hit on the head by a cricket ball but it was alright it was just stunned and flew away when it woke up.

He asks John what he wants and heads to the bar for another. While waiting for some locals to be served he thinks about the scene before he'd left. She'd asked why can't you just stay at home. She swore at him black and blue till she'd used up all her swear words and he left. In the midst of his reverie he hears a thread of conversation from a man at a table who's saying that fifteen hundred left last week and he turns to him to ask what he meant but the conversation has moved on and he doesn't.

Instead he wakes on a cliff above an ocean that crashes

against the rocks below, swirls and recedes before the next breaker. He gets painfully to his feet. It's as if he's been in a fight. He notices a town in darkness below him. There are beams of sunlight shooting across the heavens but the sun hasn't broken the horizon just yet. Suddenly he is possessed by an intense fear of the sunrise and wants to find a dark crevice to hide in but there are none to be found. He doesn't know if he can take the sunrise but has no choice. The fall from the cliff into the depths below seems the easier prospect. He peers over the edge and vertigo attacks him. He grits his teeth and buries his face in the turf to hold the panic in.

After, he shambles past the closed first and last pub and down into the town. He calls her and she asks where are you? He says Land's End. I want you to come home and he says ok. As he steps onto the bus the driver asks where he's going. He notices that there is chewing gum on the floor and he replies home. He sits at the back and grips the hand rail of the seat in front a bit too tightly. He lets go to pick up a 1p coin from the floor. He wants to laugh and cry and does not look out the window.

She puts the phone down and goes to let the pigeon out of its loft. It sweeps away above the council block and is lost in the sun. She cleans the loft out and decides she has enough time to have a cup of tea before calling the pigeon back. For a change she sits in her front reception room with her tea and woman's mag full of celebrities and royals. She looks up. Walking on the road is the woman she first saw outside the old medieval pub. She has the look of a juggernaut in her agonized and weird procession as she jerks manically forwards and back.

LIZ DEMBROWSKY

"wherever i go..."

wherever i go the same sun shines above
so closer, further, higher or lower
wherever i am — so is it

> — a tortilla
> — a saucer, or
> — a jazz record painted and thrown into the sky

one globe there —
another here

KATE DERIGHT

History of foreplay

Thousands of years ago
and a thousand footsteps away
from the gentle, curled edge
of the Cenote's
crystal white rock ripple walls
the emerald pool of soft and deadly water,
they painted a virgin
dusty wedgwood
and gave her a potion from plant root and flowers
to twist up her sobriety
and the corners of her mouth

That first splash,
I imagine,
was some surprise to the water

Afterwards he must have held his waves
and tried to stop his walls from shimmering
so no more beating, sprawling, smiling buds
would fade from blue to brown to white
in his infinitied bottom of perfect turquoise

I imagine his nausea
at the sound of the song,
the scents of the green jungle feast,
the vibration pounding down the path
and his breath
as one untouched blue ankle
teased him over the edge of the ledge

and his pain as her toes stabbed through
his hope-filled and still top
and the madness
and the waves of the sweet potion imbedded in their
girls' skin
and the softness and quiet that drowned out the
singing and the sky

After years of the inevitable addiction
the silence
and the sucked out hole of permanent craving

*

A scream from the temple reached his lip as a whisper
in the shape of Cortes:
first in wonder, then in disbelief
and finally in hatred

How confused he must have been when he saw the first
brown baby scarred with blue eyes
when it got hard to see who to blame
when his giant teacup belly stayed empty

Cortes and the conquistadores
with their syphilitic helmets and strange smells
their ugly round heads and pale skin
hurting the ground for gold
and leaving a Chichen Itza too empty
to have any sacrifice left in it

*

A breath came with the new vibration
except there were
stinking oil stains and metal
the hum of thousands of
rubber feet everyday
every one a mestizo
laughing at the ancient intentional
flat forehead and broad nose beauty

The numbness sometimes gets parted
by a scent of hope
a valiant girl in a virgin shade
steps from behind the chain of small insurance
they've placed over the diving board
and breathes for the first time
how enchanting waiting to give can be

DREADLOCK ALIEN

Anglo Indo Caribbean

I'm an Anglo Indo Caribbean,
As so me ansa dem who seh "A whe u cam fram?"
Let me tell u lickle story
Call it histri lesson,
A me dem come fi tell u bout indentured Indian.

Una all hear of slavery an its abolition,
Well a who den plant u sugar?
A de One Indian.

Me great great grandma Solanta Bika was her name,
Tricked from her homeland never to see again,
Passage from India, exchanged at Liverpool docks,
Paraded like a caatwalk queen
Den lack back up a stacks

Stacks

Stack…

A she did breed wi coolie stack,
Me grandpa mek money pan butcher's black
Send me puppa to go to school,
Prove e was no yardie fool.

Come to Henglan   tt   tt   tt   1964   tt   tt   tt
Not long before they close the door.
Flew over on an apprenticeship,
Pack up im clothes and him pack up im grip,

Yeah u know u going on a one-way trip,
Put up your foot man, u deserve it.

But wait...

Second generation   now   is revealing
Blackness all of a sudden is culturally appealing.
As my children get lighter and lighter
The future looks whiter and whiter!
Me bawl... a few drops of colour inna white paint pot,
Stir it for a decade, u will see it not.
The policy of labour migration
Followed by a process of assimilation,
Ask yourself the question
Will this really lead to a multicoloured nation?
Will it even lead to a one world nation?
Or simply the birth of a less dark English creation?

MOHAMAD 'FARDAD' GILANCHI

Faith, love, cynicism, hope, realism and an overdose of rationalism, or, The Cup

The cup is mostly cream with brown edges. Coffee drips stand as proof of its use. The cup is a cup because people call it cup. The cup is made of clay.

Sunlight glances off its glassy glaze. I know it has a handle but I can't see it from here. I can see a plate of biscuits reflected on its side. I see its handle as an ear.

Even liquid kisses can't melt the shape of a cup. The cup is a reminder of drinking whiskey and wine. I envision the Creator's hands shaping the clay. I've seen many cups like this before, they're mass-produced and you can buy them in Wilkinson's.

Human biscuits

I'm tempted to taste the tasty delicious biscuits. There's no time to talk about biscuits—all the time it's just persecution, execution, flogging people on the streets. Never biscuits. There's no time for biscuits.

More than one thousand journalists have disappeared—I think they put them into the biscuits—they cooked them all, mostly for exporting to other countries—England, America, Germany, all around the world.

The smell of biscuits is for poor people, the eating and tasting for rich people in their warm homes.

SUCAT GOLDING

I refugee

My words have little meaning
in this country
I am refugee
I am here to stay,
to build a life.
My ears and eyes are keys,
my words have little meaning in this country.

I am guttural
is difficult,
not easy
to speak
the way you say.

My parents did not die
in this country.
My parents are not dead
to me.

The burning
still
has much effect
on me.
I am refugee.

LETIZIA GRAMAGLIA

Nonna

in un breve infinito
il tempo si dissolve
e memorie dimenticate
danzano
in un vortice di sensazioni paralizzanti e soavi
a'nonn', a'nenn', a nnonn'.

smarrimento, paura e dolore
vedono un'alba tremante
attraverso occhi pregni di lacrime
mentre la prima goccia di pioggia
caduta sul mondo
taglia come diamante
vetri di limpido lattice.

parole sepolte
suoni cari e lontani
carezze e profumo di tronchi mai stanchi
di mani di cera
rugosi e speziate
a'nonn', a'nenn', a nnonn'.

lo spettro nello specchio
assente e lontano.

membra pesanti
staccate e spossate

il ventre lacerato

Grandma

in a brief infinity
time crawls away
and forgotten memories
dance
in a whirl of soft paralyzing sensations
a'nonn', a'nenn', a nnonn'.

loss, fear and grief
see their trembling dawn
through pregnant eyes
while the first drop of rain
fallen on earth
carves like diamond
glasses of limpid latex.

buried words,
ancient beloved sounds,
scent and touch of never-tired trunks,
of wax hands
wrinkled and spicy
a'nonn', a'nenn', a nnonn'.

the ghost in the mirror
absent and far.

heavy limbs
loose and exhausted.

the womb torn

dal fiume della vita che muore

carne, sangue, ossa, memoria
sulla schiena di un corpo
che e' stato e sara'

treccia di lunghi capelli grigi
sulla cima di passate sinuose forme
canti e preghiere
ritmati da labbra sbiancate
mentre il rosario scorre
tra dita d'avorio.

teneri occhi
smarriti sotto il velo del tempo
verdi e profondi
come acque di oceani sereni

dall'antica materna montagna
un canto gioioso di addio
a'nonn', a'nenn', a nnonn'
la voce avvolgente di pini senza tempo
testimoni del passaggio
di avi a me cari.

by the stream of dying life

flesh, blood, bones, memory
on the back of a body
that was and will be.

plait of long grey hair
on the top of your once sinuous shape
songs and prayers
in the rhythm of white lips
while the rosary runs
through ivory fingers.

soft eyes
lost under the veil of time
deep and green
like waters of serene oceans

from the old motherly mountain
a joyful farewell song
a'nonn', a'nenn', a nnonn'
the enveloping voice of timeless pines
witnessing the passage
of my dear forebears.

KALA GRANT

Celebration we
(The Culinary Arts Festival, Independence Day, Ocho Rios)

Festival time come again,
An' new event deh undah tent,
"Culinary Arts Festival," dem say!
"Come see we food on display!"
Ackee and saltfish, mackerel run down,
Donkey ride, 'nancy story, dip an' fall dung!
Grater cake fi set dem straight,
Jackass Jawbone fi di mout' pirate.
Fish escoveitch, pork and chicken jerk,
Traditional stalls fi give we pride perk!
But wait? Is wah dis me buck up pon come see?
"Evita's Rasta Pasta? But kiss me wharra what'sit doh eeh?"
Rastah wah? Evita who?
But a weh dis Italian bangarang come yah fi do?
"Liza, listen weh dah twist up mout' European refugee,
Jump off a' banana boat an' a tell we!"
"Welcome everybody to my mama mia stall!
I have Rasta Pasta for us all!
Let me demonstrate for you,
How to make it Italivoo!"
Missis, you waan fi see di Jamaican red 'kin people dem,
Dah ooh and dah aah pon di pasta pengeleng!
An' poonkus pon pankas,
Here comes the black bougivoo,
Dah ask all kinda question 'bout di woman plastic food!
"Me say, ah shame so till di day fi see me owna people dem!"
Dem dash way blue drawers and boil pum-pum yam,
Dem step over we bammy and we St Mary Lacatan

Celebration we

Festival time is here again and there is a new event under the tent they call "Culinary Arts Festival" where we will see our food on display.

Dishes such as Ackee and Saltfish and mackerel run down (coconut based stew with salted meat or fish) plus donkey rides and Anancy stories. Everyone dancing to the dip and fall back! (dip and fall back—a folk song to which a traditional dance is done—similar to 'bruckings')

Fish will be escovietched (fish fried with a pickled sauce of hot scotch bonnet pepper, onion rings, pimento seeds), there will be jerk pork and chicken plus traditional stalls to make us even more proud! But wait one minute! What is this I see in front of me? Evita's Italian Rasta Pasta? But what is this?

Rasta what? Evita who? But what has this Italian comical display come here to do? Liza, listen to what that twisted mouth European refugee, who jumped off the banana boat, is saying to us.

"Welcome everyone to my..."

Miss, you should have seen the Jamaican red skinned people (a colloquial term for mulatto or light skinned blacks) exclaiming at the pasta concoction.

Dem spit pon tu'n cornmeal and roas' corn
Ah never see we tu'n fool so, from ah born!
Missis, me dis look pon we and shake me head,
'Cause festival for Independence drop stiff stone dead!!
Instead of dem dah do celebration 'We',
Jamaican Festival tu'n dependent on a foreign spree!

And to make matters worse, here come the middle class blacks asking all kinds of questions about the plastic food!

I say, I was so ashamed that day to see my own people. They threw away blue drawers (cornmeal *pone*—done in banana leaves) and boiled pum-pum yam (yes, a yam named after a woman's private parts—only because the skin appears hairy—roots everywhere), they stepped over the bammy (cassava cake) and the St. Mary Lacatan (a type of banana), they spat at turned cornmeal and roasted corn! I have never seen us become so stupid like this since I was born!

My dear, I just looked on us and shook my head, because Festival for Independence was stiff stone dead! Instead of us doing celebration WE, Jamaican festival has become dependent on a foreign fancy!

Dat black model
(for Alex Wek)

Now take for example dat black model,
Coo pon she wid her big broad lip
Her black till she purple skin,
Her face roun' like moon
Her nose big like di setting sun
Coo pon she! Bout she deh pon catwalk
I want to know if dem tek we fe poppyshow!
How dare dem white people throw our blackness ina
we face like dat?
First dem tek we from we homelan' inna big ship,
Change we name to Mr and Mrs so an' so
Rape we mental to form twisted images of Europe in our
African form,
Change di colour of we Jesus,
Tell us our 'newly' acquired long hair, hook nose
Thin lips...
Our whitewashed skin and light brown or if you lucky
Grey, blue eyes are the true image of beauty.
An' now, all of a sudden they messing wid me minds!
They start to put our bastard features on show
Like Hottentot backside under English throne!
They throwing we blackness in *our* face?
They making us know say we no so black no more
Cause we can't even look ina di eye o' di past an' see we
true African self?
I can't tek see di gyal inna di bright, bright, shocking
colours dem,
A walk up and down wid di res' of di 'rexic looking gyal
dem
She know how fool she look or what?

Look how me brown an' nice?
You never see me a wear dem deh outrageous colours
deh.
So who give her the right?
Why di gyal don't straighten her hair an' look decent.
Dis short picky-picky head business,
Before she grow her hair an' look like somebody!
It's not fair I tell you!
Why is she free to be African?
Free to be black?
Why not me too?
I would look good on the catwalk!

THE JIGSAW GROUP
(Coventry Refugee Centre)

"I used to live in the bedroom..."

I used to live in the bedroom
Now I live in the bathroom
Because I like water

(Ajmal, Farid, Hawar and Hosein)

Kicking melons

Kicking melons in the garden. Ajmal is in goal. Hosein
has the melon. The melon is called Hawar.

Hosein goes to score a goal. He shoots.
Hawar breaks with a splut and explodes.

He bursts like
a green balloon and
red and green and black spill out.

(Ajmal, Hawar and Hosein)

Crashing cars

Suicide
Airbag on fall
Shatter
Flame beauty
Tree falls
Car engine explodes
Wheels roll away
Cool way to die
Easy/quick

Alone in space
Entering black hole
Unlucky
Girly screaming
Terrified
Example of Fatmir

(Fatmir)

I kill you in America

I kill you in America
You stole my money
You're running away
I chased you by car and I follow
You in America
You can't run
I killed you in America

(Ajmal, Farid, Hawar and Hosein)

Cool blood

When this began
I was looking at the stars
Wondering, *Where the hell's my roof?*
And thinking about Mars.

The dead will walk the earth
When hell is full
In five years, you watch,
They will.

When this began
I had nothing to say
Nothing to eat
Nowhere to stay.

I was in care
'Cos my parents were dead
Eaten alive
In their bed.

The dead will walk the earth
When hell is full
In five years, you watch,
They will.

They used their bones
As toothpicks
And ate their flesh
With spiky sticks.

I looked at the stars
And found out that
My parents were alive
But they had no heads.

The dead will walk the earth
When hell is full
In five years, you watch,
They will.

(Ayesha, Fatmir, Geeta, Lucy and Uzair)

I am not asleep

I am scared in the night
Because I watched a scary film

Vampires sucked people's blood
Invisible ghosts chased us
With swords making scary noises
I saw a man killed by a knife

I am not asleep I never sleep
I've forgotten how to sleep
I've forgotten what time it is

(Ajmal, Farid, Hawar and Hosein)

Man of the match

He takes his clothes and shoes off. Then he puts on his football boots. Ties his laces. Gets up. Picks up his T-shirt, puts it on, rubs the dust from his shirt.

He opens the door, goes out, the crowd cheers and claps their hands. He dances, thinks he's number one. He runs, shows off his skills, he kicks and starts fighting, he shouts, "Yes, yes, yes!" and he shoots and the ball goes through the goalie's legs.

He gets a gun out, he shoots at people, he looks for someone to kill, he shoots people to get the ball, he says he's heavy, he goes to shoot, he hits the goalie in the face. He fights with the goalie, throws him out of the way and scores. Then he sings the James Bond song, shoots into the crowd.

He sees the scoreboard, they're winning by a million goals, he's happy. He salutes the crowds, takes a picture of the crowd and the scoreboard, then he kills the commentator.

(Mohamed and Uzair)

"Swimming is like suffocating..."

Swimming is like suffocating.
It's like when you are in the deep of
water you can't breath out.
It's like a strange man is killing you
  in a dark cave
    a strange man with a big face and
      big eyes big nose suffocating you
        with a big chair. A cave with
noises—his voice is really rough,
he looks like a green monster—
sounds like birds and
  bears and lions and bats, sounds
    making a strange big voice.
      The man was a bit scary.
        I have to kill the man and
          I have to take something big
            to kill the man. When you
              are coming out you feel like
                you are breathing. It feels
                  better because you are breathing
                    now. I have to play with
                the water. I feel free and never
                  go to the deep end.

(Tariro)

55

Oh beer

Because I don't like the smell of
beer I hate it and I would never drink
when I grow up by the way it makes you feel
dizzy and you can't see where you're
going you can say what you want
to another person and in the
morning when they said what you said
you won't believe because you were drunk.

I would shout to them and tell
him don't get near me if he/she is
sleeping with me I would run home
because drunk people could do what
they want so I don't get near them or
I'll throw cold water at them to cool
down if not take them straight to bed
if he/she shouts at me I'll tell them
to shut-up or let them say what they
want and ignore them.

(Anisa)

"Sleeping is like baking a pancake…"

Sleeping is like baking a pancake
                         being surrounded by
your own army. Thoughtless thoughts.
It's like forgetting your day,
                         throwing a bunch
        of flowers from your hand
        letting go of a rope you're holding

                baking a pancake
                because smelling a pancake
        on Saturday morning
        breakfast feels familiar
                         and knowing
        what's going on gives control.
                Having your own
        army
                         is protecting,
                makes you feel safe.

                Thoughtless thoughts
        because dreams
        make no sense
when you've forgotten,
        woken up.

(Ayesha)

Farid

Farid smiles a lot,
       is like a cheeky bird stealing biscuits.

(Trevor)

Lucy

Lucy have got big legs like an
old person sleeping on bench

Lucy is clear-the-plates
wash-the-hand

(Farid and Trevor)

The flash

A tragic day. Lumily the baby was travelling on a plane to Jamaica. She was going to visit her grandmother and all her family were with her. She had five brothers and six sisters. It was a rainy day, with wind, thunderstorms and huge waves on the ocean below.

Lumily was looking out of the window over the Atlantic when a flash of lightning hit the aeroplane's wing and the plane bounced and bounced and turned and turned round and tumbled down in a nose dive and sank deep into the ocean. Lumily drowned.

Then her new life began. She saw people walking through doors and she wanted to see what was behind the doors, so she decided to see for herself. She walked through the door that was nearest to her, with the most people going through it. As she walked through it she felt excited and nervous.

She started to shake and her bone structure changed. She looked down to see two orange paws and when she looked up she saw jungle all around her. In front of her there was a large pond. She walked over to it and saw her face in the water. She was a tiger. She had a crown on her head.

(Uzair)

MAZHAR KHALIK

France

After debates
And long deliberations
The French banned religious symbols
From the schools.

Afterwards,
in an interview
a teenaged Muslim girl
said something in French.

I think she was angry.

Dem a call de place... 'Hillfields'
AMAL ABDOSHA

Joseph
MARGARET GATURU

We are here to stay!
MARGARET GATURU

Samira & Yawa
HABIBA ABDEL-NOUR

The Garden of International Friendship
KULSI SYAL

Malika
SHAHIN CHAFOURI

THE LULA G YOUTH GROUP

The likes

busy like people busy like me
busy like raindrops that's heavy, that is
noisy like the Statue of Liberty
noisy like the horn

stupid like Lady Godiva
sexy like my looks my voice
sexy like my shoes

McDonalds like greasy
girls like whoa!
carparks like silence, dirty like tramps
& all the lovely pollution in the air

FRANCKY LUNGANGA

Le soleil

Roi soleil maître de temps, Roi soleil maître de circonstance.
Roi soleil commendeur de la détente.
Ton couché consacre l'arrêt de travail,
le début de l'œuvre de ténèbre,
de l'obscurité ce noir opaque
qui effroie l'homme malgré sa taille;
les maîtres des maisons ferment leurs portes
et les mères couvrent leurs petits.

A six heures boule de feu d'un orange pâle,
tu reveille le coq et suscite son chant.
A midi, tu atteint l'apogé de ta magnificience
en brûlant la peau. Astre roi personne ne peut
lever les yeux pour couvrir ton champ.
Le soir, comble de douceur tu rassemble
les amoureux au bord du fleuve! Astre fugeant,
tu laisses libre cours au voleur pour assouvir ses penchants.

King Sun

King Sun master of weather, King Sun master of circumstance.
King Sun commander of the détente.
Your setting consecrates the close of play,
begins the work of darkness,
this black fog of obscurity
that frightens man, despite his power;
the master of the house shuts his door,
mothers shield their children.

At six o' clock, ball of pale orange fire
you awaken the cock, breathe life into his song.
At noon, your magnificence attains its apogee,
burning our skin. Star king, no-one
may raise his eyes to scan your field.
In the evening, full of sweetness
you bring together lovers on the riverbank!
Fleeing star, you set thieves free to satisfy their habits.

Ceci est pour toi...

Ceci est pour toi prêtresse de Onya Shongo source de
vie.
Digne mortier duquel farine fin je suis sorti, laisse moi te
rendre hommage.
Innitiatrice venérée, au culte de la vie tu m'initia,
à la vénération de la femme déesse comme toi tu
m'entraîna.

Ceci est pour toi belle de Katako,
belle à la beauté farouche des forêts vierges de Congo.
De ton cousin le wenge, bois noir tu as tiré cette teinte
maronne symbole de repos.
De ta cousine la girafe au long cou tu as pris la grâce.
De ta tante la lionne tu as reçu la noblesse.
De ton oncle le fleuve Congo, tu as hérité la majesté.
Du Nyirangongo le volcan ton frère tu as obtenu la
splendeur.
De l'okapi ta soeur tu as volé cette aisance à la limite de la
suffisance.

Ceci est donc pour toi porte par laquelle je decouvris le
monde.
Ceci est donc pour toi objet de toute ma gratitude.
Ceci est pour toi, ma mère et mon tout.

This is for you...

This is for you, priestess of Onya Shongo, source of life.
Deserving mortar from which fine grain I grew, let me
praise you.
Venerated instructress, you initiated me in the cult of
life,
you trained me to venerate goddess-women like you.

This is for you, belle of Katako,
belle of the fierce beautiful Congo's virgin forests.
From your cousin the black wood *wenge* you took your
brown colour, symbol of rest.
From your long-necked cousin the giraffe you took your
grace.
From your aunt the lioness you received your nobility.
From your uncle the river Congo you inherited your
majesty.
From Nyirangongo the volcano your brother came your
splendour.
From the okapi your sister you stole your pride.

This then is for you, door by which I discovered the
world.
This then is for you, object of all my gratitude.
This is for you, my mother, my all.

ARSALAN MIRZA

My name is Arsalan. I come from Iraq. I have five brothers and one sister. My father died in 1984. I come to U.K. 21/12/1999. My brothers Shakwan and Karwan are living in Holland and my sister Marewan is living in Norway. I am not married.

I am an interpreter at Coventry Refugee Centre. I speak four languages: for Kurdish people, Arabic, Afghani and Farsi. These people come to the Refugee Centre with problems with housing and money and solicitors and the home office.

I am so happy in Coventry Refugee Centre to help refugee people. All refugees are the same for me. And I am happy the people ask me for help.

I am happy in Coventry. I like sometimes to go to the Peace House to see my friends, and also I like the cathedral, because it is an old building. It is very nice and every day a lot of people go to see this building. Inside the building they have a big hole in the wall and there is an altar. In the wall they have very nice writings.

MANASHA MOHAMED

The sun is shining like a fire in the sky

The storm comes so quickly that nobody notices.
The children play outside on the wet ground using the
water to have a bath.
All people go outside to enjoy the fresh rainwater.
The animals run away from the rain to their stalls.
When they hear the storm they worry about their calves.
The thunder comes quickly and the animals run away.
It leaves without causing any disaster.

Robin Bhechargadud

From when I was in Somalia I remember many kinds of
birds. When the weather was hot, I saw the robin near
my house and when the wind whooshed the robin
swayed and made a sound like music: chip-chip-chip.
"What a beautiful robin," I said. I wanted to be her friend
and every day I would meet her and listen to her song.

After the wind stopped she came down into the grass
looking for something to eat. I looked through the
window. When she noticed me she fluttered quickly
away to touch the golden moon.

ALBERTO ORENGO

*A mio zio **Palo**: racconto di guerra*

Un giorno incontro un vecchio.
Mi racconta della guerra
mi vedo allo specchio.
E' entrato ragazzo
in quella galleria di delirio.
S'ammazzavano da una parte
all'altra della valle e poco prima
si scambiavano formaggio e farina.
Il suo fucile era alto, per non colpire,
era buono lui.
Poi d'Otranto le onde,
i muli buttati a mare che annegano,
i loro occhi atterriti.
giù, sempre più giù, finché anche le nari
scompaiono nella schiuma arrabbiata.

S'interrompe.

I suoi occhi,
Dio quei suoi occhi di vecchio…

Guardo la stufa rovente
odore buono di legna
calore, castagne.
Gli fisso le mani.
Sono grandi e nodose le sue mani.
Le sue dita radici nel mio
stupore.

To my uncle **Palo**: *a war tale*

One day I meet an old man.
He tells me about the war
I see myself in a mirror.
He was a boy when he came into
that tunnel of madness.
       They killed one another across the valley,
while the day before
they exchanged flour and cheese.
His shotgun was kept high lest he could kill,
he was a good man in fact.
Then the waves of *Otranto*,
the mules thrown overboard, sinking,
the terror in their eyes.
Down, down, until even their nostrils
are sucked down by the enraged foam.

       He stops.

His eyes,
God those old man's eyes…

       I gaze at the red-hot stove
good smell of wood
warmth, chestnuts.
I gaze at his hands.
Big and knotted are his hands.
His fingers are roots in my
bewilderment.

L'Albania, i Carpazi
il furore
di una battaglia notturna,
il cannone infuocato
il compagno accasciato.
Notti gelide di vedetta
il gelo, il calore di avide boccate
di sigaretta.
Un pacco alla settimana,
"campione raccomandato senza valore"
qualcosa di buono da casa,
"avvolto in carta da confezioni d'alta classe."
"*ricevuti tutti*".
CASA
parola ottenebrante come l'oppio,
rimbomba così forte nel cranio.

Dannata guerra,
in quanti l'hanno già detto.

Le sue lacrime, poi,

il silenzio stordente.
Nella stufa crepitio di legna.

Il racconto continua in un silenzio irreale.
Fiume!
si salvi chi può!
Si torna a casa
Il deserto bianco scampato,
un ritorno sofferto,
di casale in casale
in cerca di scarpe.

Albany, the Carpathians
the rage
of a night battle,
the red-hot field-gun
his comrade slumped to the ground.
Freezing nights on the lookout
cold. Warmth of greedy drags
of smoke.
One parcel a week,
"registered sample post"
something good from home.
"Tailored and wrapped in high-class paper."
"got them all".
HOME
a word which muddles like opium
so loud it booms into your skull.

Bloody war,
how many have already said that?

His tears. Then,

the stunning silence.
In the stove the crackling of wood.

The tale goes on in a dreamlike silence.
Fiume!
Every man for himself!
Let's go home,
Escape from the White Desert,
a hard home-coming
through farmhouses and hamlets
searching for the right shoes.

Angosciosa e infinita marcia solitaria
di uno scheletro che vaga nella nebbia.
Gli scarponi militari da nascondere,
una caviglia rotta, piedi sfatti
in scarpe non sue.
Solitudine padana
Una Stazione
Nelle sue parole, gli sguardi
di chi parte per
l'inferno.

E poi casa,
ma di notte,
come il topo nel granaio.
E di giorno in un buco, ubriaco
del profumo di fieno, il profumo di libertà,
di pace.

Questa che vi ho raccontato
è la sua guerra,
la sua memoria nella mia,
La mia nella vostra.
Questa è la storia già scordata.

La mia tristezza
è il suo sorriso su una lapide.

Ma le sue lacrime di vecchio,
le sue lacrime d'argento,
me le porto via
e le affido al vento.

The excruciating endless walk
of a skeleton wandering in the fog.
Military boots to hide
a broken ankle, worn feet
in someone else's shoes.
Loneliness of the Po Valley
a train station
in his words the eyes
of those leaving
for hell.

Then home,
but just for the night
like a mouse in the barn,
then everyday in a hole, drunk with
the smell of hay from outside,
the smell of freedom, of peace.

        What I've just told you
is his war,
his memory in mine,
mine in yours.
This is the forgotten story.

My grief
is his smile on a tombstone.

        But his old man's tears,
his tears of silver,
I'll bring with me
and entrust to the wind.

ROY PARGETTER

Curry delight
(An extract from his forthcoming novel **The Rock House Nutter***)*

Friday night was approaching, so me and Sue got ready to meet up with Eddie and Dawn. We were at the concert hall at the Willenhall Club, a great place back then in the Seventies. We had a game of bingo—never won fuck all but it was a good laugh. For the rest of the night we talked to each other, and then Sue and Dawn would get up and dance. Later on we agreed to go to the Rock House and have a mad night up there. While in the Willenhall Club a couple of hours went by, and a lot of our friends who we knew came there and sat by us. As we were talking away and reminiscing about some of the things what I got up to in the Rock House, and things we all got up to from years past, Dawn's mum Kitty came and sat down with us. Kitty was a real nice person and a good laugh. On many future occasions Sue would ask Kitty if she had a spare fag on her. We were all in the same boat, not much money and always skint. Around 10:30 the four of us went to town and went straight away to the Rock House where we started drinking Pernod. While dancing and having a good time I seen the two bouncers, Shit Head and Dick Face, and they looked over but there was no trouble. We had a good night that night and we all arranged to meet up the following Saturday and do it all over again.

The next week came and me and Sue walked over to Eddie and Dawn's flat. When we got there they were having an argument about money. Me and Sue took no notice as they would do this on many occasions, like most couples do.

Now Dawn's a really nice person, and just like Sue she was good looking in her day, and they still look good now. Dawn always gave as good as Eddie gave her, and that night she didn't want to spend the money. "Fuck this, we're going out," said Eddie, and with saying that he rips the door off its hinges and throws it outside on the grass. Then he picks up the television, says "Fuck this lump of shit," and throws it straight out of the window.

"That will save you buying a licence," I said to him. We all started laughing.

"Sit down," he said to Sue and me, "I'll make you a cup of tea." Dawn had settled down by now. Eddie brought the tea, said he'd be back in an hour and went off round Willenhall to scrounge some money. To his mum's first, and then his mates, and so on.

After getting enough money we all went to the Willenhall Club. When we arrived the group was playing a Showaddywaddy tune, *Under the Moon of Love*. We got a pint and a short each and Sue got pissed quickly. The bingo had just started, and the first number to be called was Kelly's eye, number one.

"Here you are!" Sue shouts, and holds her tickets up and everyone started laughing and she thought this was funny.

"What the fuck are you doing?" I asked, and with that remark Eddie and Dawn were in bits laughing.

No one won anything that night, and sitting there in front of us were these two lads. A while later one of them came over to me and said "You owe me one pound fifty."

"Piss off," I said. "What are you on about, mate?" Ten minutes later he came over again and said the same thing, then he sat down. I decided to go over to where he was sitting with my pint, and then pouring it over his head I said "That's 50p's worth, I'll give you the other pound next week."

"You fucking wanker," he said and pissed off home. Me and Sue started rowing and all the others were howling with laughter. A while later this bald chap called Les said to Eddie that he knew Sue and explained that he had just split up with his wife. He asked if he could sit down with us, and Eddie agreed, thinking it was a friend of Sue's. Sue then said "Who the fuck is that chap?"

"He said he knows you from somewhere," replied Eddie.

"I can't remember him," Sue said. Les started saying to Sue and Dawn that he's rich, and he's got this American car.

"So fucking what?" I said.

"I'll have a double brandy," said Sue.

"I'll have the same," said Dawn.

"Does anyone else want a drink?" Les asked, and with that we all put our orders in.

A while later we were all getting pissed and were ready to go to the Rock House. We all got a taxi there, and Les paid for that thanks to the charms of Sue and Dawn. On arriving at the Rock House we all got straight into the shit lift. You would go eight feet up and then all of a sudden drop back down two fuckers. Eventually going into the main ballroom they were playing *Dancing Queen*, the Abba classic. Sue and Dawn got Les to buy us all drinks again, and we sat down. Me and Eddie decided to go upstairs to drink some Pernod. Walking towards the stairs we seen Albert, Andy, Chris and a few others; even Johnny was there, pissed as a fart and still nicking beer from the stage, lucky bastard. After we finished chatting with the lads me and Eddie went upstairs to the bar. We started drinking beer at first and then we started on the shorts. It was Eddie's round, and he asked me "What short are you having, Roy?"

"Anything," I replied, "as long as it gets me fucking pissed." The next minute over comes Eddie with three shorts apiece, laughing his head off. As we stood on the balcony looking over I could see Sue and Dawn down below dancing away. They looked up and waved to us both. As me and Eddie were looking at the other women dancing away and seeing if we could recognise anyone, I went over to the bar and got a glass of ice and said to Eddie, "Watch this fucker." I threw it all over the dancefloor underneath us, and as ice hit floor it went all over the place. Within seconds all these people were slipping over and sliding about everywhere, and everyone was laughing and wondering what the fuck was going on. Me and Eddie were crying with laughter, we thought it was so funny. The bouncers were looking around and trying to suss out what was going on but they never clicked on at all. Fuck it, I thought, I'll go and get some more ice and give it another go. I threw the ice on the dancefloor, still laughing, then said to Eddie that we had better go downstairs to see Sue and Dawn. Off we went. A fight had broken out on the stairs and seemed to be getting a bit messy.

"Let's go over and see what's going on," Eddie said.

"Bollocks to them," I replied, "let them sort it out themselves."

When we met up with Sue and Dawn they were sitting down having a fag. I said to them, "Where's that baldy twat gone?"

"He's pissed off somewhere," said Dawn. "He said he might be back later." As me and Eddie sat down to have a smoke and a drink we were deciding whether to have something to eat or do a taxi run, as we did not have enough money for both. We both agreed that we would get a taxi home at the end of the night instead. Eddie said, "I'll be back in a minute. I'm off to the bar to get some drink for us." I decided to get Sue and Dawn up for a dance, and as we were dancing away to a Suzy Quattro record I started looking upwards towards the glitter ball above as it shone everywhere around. Being pissed as a fart I forgot where I was and careered off in the wrong direction, falling over by a table round the outskirts of the dancefloor. As I got up I was laughing my head off. Sue came over. "For fuck's sake, sit down." We sat down and Eddie bought us drinks. He couldn't stop laughing as he had seen what had happened. I said to everyone, "Let's drink up and fuck off home." Everyone agreed and a while later we started to leave the Rock House. As we were walking along to where the toilets were me and Eddie picked up a pint glass apiece and then looked at each other and started to eat the glass. After taking a few big chunks from the beer glasses I could see Sue and Dawn getting annoyed at us both. "Fucking silly bastards," they said. We were laughing at them with the blood coming from our mouths.

Going out of the Rock House and towards the taxi rank I happened to turn my head, looking down the alleyway situated between the City Arms and the shop next door and who should I see down there but Ronnie S trying to get his leg over with some tart. It was raining hard as we walked down to where the big Boots store used to be. Sue fell over in the road as she as singing *New York New York* while walking along the curb. She got up laughing, but her clothes were all shitted up. "I'm not going home until I've cleaned myself up," she said. Just then this chap walked past and asked if she was alright. "And you can fuck off as well mate,"

Sue replied. Everybody was howling with laughter.

Off we went to the taxi rank and when we got there Sue and Dawn took a diversion, going upstairs into the curry house so Sue could get cleaned up in the toilets. Just then Baldy Les came over and asked what we were up to.

"Just waiting for Sue and Dawn to come out of the toilets, then get a taxi home," Eddie replied.

"I'll pay for the taxi," he said. After waiting ten minutes there was still no sign of Sue and Dawn. "Fuck this," I said, and we decided to go and see where they had got to. Walking up the stairs and sitting ourselves down in the restaurant, this waiter came over and said, "No drink, no table."

"Let's just fuck off," I said, but then Sue and Dawn came out of the toilets, saw us and sat down, still singing the same bastard record, *New York New York*. The waiter came over again and asked what we were going to order. Les then ordered drinks for us all as there was no way Sue and Dawn were going to leave in a hurry. We all sat there drinking and talking loudly.

"You can order something to eat, but not loads," Les said. "I'll be back in a minute. I'm just popping to the pub next door for some fags."

"I've got no money," I replied. "You'd better come back, you little bastard. There's no way I'm cleaning the fucking dishes all night long."

"That won't happen. You're not ordering that much." And off he went.

Eddie looked at me. "What did he just say, Roy?"

I replied, with a smile on my face, "Order what you want."

We all looked at the menu and ordered straight away. We had curry and rice, followed by steak, chips and peas, and a side salad. Sue and Dawn had a chicken curry, a bottle of wine and Bombay Duck, and to all you thick bastards, that's fish. A while later there's still no sign of Les. The waiter brought the food over and we all got stuck in. First the curry and rice with lots of wine and beer. We were all cracking jokes, laughing and playing up. The manager came over and asked "Could you all calm down a bit please, there's people in here trying to eat." Just then Les came back and his eyes started protruding from his head. "What the fuck have you ordered?" he asked. Well, the tears were rolling down our faces with laughter and before Les could say anything I replied to the manager, "This man's paying for our food, aren't you mate?" Les turned round to the manager and said in a shocked voice, "Bollocks. I suppose I am." He could do no more but sit down and watch, and he didn't seem a very happy man at all. Just then the waiter came back over with the rest of our order, and put the food on the tale with more beer. "Fucking hell," we all heard, "who's that lot for?" as Les sunk into depression.

As we got stuck into our main courses and our drinks we were having a ball. The meal was fit for a king and it was all free. As I started cutting my steak I realised the knife was blunt so I called the waiter over to change it. Then I got stuck in and started cutting my steak. Not realising how sharp the new knife was I pushed down hard with my fork and started cutting. A moment later it slipped and everything went everywhere. The chips and peas flew off the plate and ended up on the floor, and some of it even went on the next table. "You bastard," I said in a loud voice, and everyone there, bar a few, was howling with laughter. Some of the looks we got from other people were evil, but who gives a fuck when you're enjoying yourselves? Les sat there and said, "I've never seen people act like that."

"Chill out, you twat," I said to him, which started us laughing even more.

Me, Eddie and Dawn were just getting back to normal when Sue called the waiter over and ordered another bottle of wine, which started it all off again. Just then the manager came over, waving his arms frantically and in broken English said "Calm down, you are all crazy."

"Well," I replied to him, "we are from Willenhall."

"Willenhall!" he said, putting his finger to his head. "Eat your food and get out. You're all fucking crazy!" As he was saying this I got off my chair and started to pick up all the peas and chips from off the floor and put them onto a plate, only to drop it again. By this time the four of us were well pissed and the place was in chaos. Soon it was time to leave as the manager was getting angry and preparing to call the police. Failing that we could have ended up in tomorrow's curry, he was that mad with us.

After a good night it was time for Les to pay the bill, and when he got it he was not amused. He turned to us and said he could not pay for it all and would have to use his credit card. "What's the problem?" Eddie asked him. Les then explained that it was not his card, it was his mate's. Naughty naughty.

"It's not our fucking problem," I said to Les, still laughing. "We only ate the fucking food." He sorted it out one way or another, and off we went to get a taxi home. In the taxi we also found out that he never had his own house and he was lodging, also that he never had any money or a credit card; also that he was a lying little bastard.

SIMA PARTOVI

Sun

Sun is the biggest star, full of warmth. When we want to say hello to somebody, especially in the morning, we say a hello as big as the sun and warm as the sun.

Sun is very big and orange in my country and you can usually see it in the sky. Full of ability, you can see the laugh of the sun and it is very happy. We have no darkness, even at night. It is very positive in my country, giving us ability and activity.

Usually when you say to children to paint something, they paint a mountain and a very big sun who is laughing. I missed it. I wished, I had it and hold it.

MARTYN RICHARDS

Soy Celto Britanico

It was New Year's Eve, the 31st December 2001.

We sat in a small bar in the Plaça Cal Font, a square only recently created from a warren of narrow streets of redundant clothing factories. Only one of those factories—the largest—had been left, refurbished beyond recognition as the town's new library and cultural centre.

Our bar was at the opposite end of the square to the library.

About twenty customers were seated at simple, rectangular tables, end-facing the two walls which projected parallel to the door. The bar counter sat in one corner, against the wall opposite ours, which was on the left hand side entering from the street.

Side by side, my wife and I faced into the bar, our backs to the window. Opposite sat a cousin to my wife. We had been there for about an hour, talking, catching up.

I must have said something to amuse her, though I do not remember what.

"Tu Inglés," she said, laughing.

Always the same thing, I sighed, shaking my head. These continentals, always calling all Britons "Inglés"— English—from the language.

"No!" I exclaimed, loud enough for some customers on the other side of the bar to turn their heads in our direction.

One of these heads presented a small-faced, black-haired, close-cropped, sallow-skinned young man of North African appearance.

"Yo no Inglés!" I cried, shaking my head.

"No?" the cousin laughingly queried.

"No!" my wife confirmed knowingly.

The sallow face rose from its table on the far side of the room, twisting its pencil-thin moustache. His other fingers rolled a thin cigarette in a self-manufacturing manner. He stood and stared at me from a metre away with a slightly challenging cynical air, saying in clear English: "Me Taliban. I like Taliban. Taliban good."

Seconds later, uninvited, he lowered his thin frame into the spare chair to my right.

His speech became so staccato I half expected him to add "Exterminate! Exterminate!" in the Dalek manner.

"England—Britain—Tony Blair—American puppets!" he scorned, a half-smiling light flickering across his eyes, but without glazing.

I shook my head, not wishing to ignite a fire where one might have been undousable. From the corner of one eye

I saw a young lady behind the bar eying our group.

My wife told our visitor, in diplomatic Spanish, that we were having an end-of-year family reunion in which he was intruding. Would he please leave us, she asked, supported by her cousin. Although not threatening, he seemed reluctant to return to his own table.

The hovering lady from the bar appeared at our table, asking if everything was "alright?"

We explained that this man had interrupted, without invitation, our family reunion, and seemed reluctant to leave us to our own privacy.

Smoke from his thin cigarette wafted across our faces.

He was at last persuaded by the bar lady to leave us. In fact, in less than a minute he had packed his few belongings from his own table into his jacket and left the premises.

"Ah!" the bar lady cried. Opening the door she ran across the near-empty darkened square. We could not discern the details of her catching up with him but a few minutes later she returned holding her money aloft.

"Leave without paying, ah!" she laughed, moving behind the counter to enter her spoils into the till, grasping a glass with shaking hand.

Some months after our return to Britain, I discovered that an enterprising agent friend had forwarded an account of this incident to the Barcelona newspaper La Vanguardia. This newspaper's nineteenth century founder, Godó, later ennobled as a Count, had originated from the same Igualada in which our encounter had occurred.

On the 24th January 2003, I heard BBC Radio including the "arrest of fourteen terrorist suspects of North African origin in and around Barcelona" in its news bulletins. Igualada is in Barcelona Province.

My mind flew back to that night, thirteen months earlier in that soft-lit bar, when the sallow Algerian had risen to my excited proclamation of my identity and crossed the room to offer something of his.

I had to ponder deeply how much of his was a cry of protest bravado, or, more seriously, whether he was one of those "fourteen" arrested in Catalunya.

I had not seen him as a violent, even arrogant, man nor, I thought, the sort to enjoy life under a Taliban-type regime. If so, why had he resorted to residency in the more tolerant modern Spain? Had he uttered his strident assertion because I seemed—probably was—the only Briton in the bar?

I now wondered if I should have asked more questions of him. They had not occurred to me at the time. We cannot re-run Time.

My assertion of my identity, to counter the misinformation about it, in some way—perhaps—

understood what could have been his real reason for his protest to me, or through me to those to whom I have told the story.

I shrink from the violence of the *guerrilla*—'little war'— but the Nations of the Sioux proved that only when they had the actual power to reclaim Wounded Knee did the 'big boys' at last listen to them.

Wounded Knee was an 'American' example, but there are more from every continent, because the 'big boys' teach others that this is the way. Australian Aborigines know, and use, more than one type of boomerang.

TIRO SEBINA

Asylum-seeker

She was born
out of the spindly thighs
of fading memory
amidst the febrile sighs
of wandering thoughts
She remains marginal
like metaphors
in discarded poems

She sips coffee
in unfamiliar climates
Her face concealing anxiety
marked by wounds
of disquiet
Her mind taxed
by the privacy
of pain

ALAN SPRUNG

Remi and the boss-man

The hooter's early morning call split the dusty, Gabon air with the certainty of a machete cracking open a coconut and dragged the boys' troubled minds from their fading dreams of home to the grim reality of slavery in the 21st Century. Remi woke amid the granite dust, the scattering of birds and the routine groans of his fellow captives, to begin the first day of his third year in the quarry. He quickly rubbed the sleep from his eyes, wiped away the salt deposits left from the tears he'd shed in the night and glanced around for any sign of the boss-man. In his waking hours, this young slave watched the boss-man like a hawk.

For two whole years, in the face of much physical punishment, he'd managed to keep quiet but that hadn't come easy. His family had always been poor and had often struggled to find sufficient food for everyone but outside of that he'd flourished in the relative freedom of Benin village life and had grown to be a strong-willed and articulate eight-year-old by the time his parents were talked into sending him to the quarry to work. Incarceration had brought the kind of feelings of anger that Remi imagined a newly captured lion must have, feelings that stirred deep inside him at the beginning of each new day, long before he was out of bed.

The familiar sound of the bunkroom door opening turned every head and Remi looked across the room hoping not to see the man he'd come to hate. He was disappointed. A large silhouette stood motionless for a second or two, blocking a doorway that was scarcely big enough to contain it. An all too familiar fear gripped Remi's young body. "Get out of here! Get out of here and get to work!"

Every under-nourished pair of legs in the place, including Remi's, joined the speedy exodus. "You lazy good-for-nothings!" barked the boss-man. "No wonder your families wanted rid of you! Get to work! Go on, get to work!"

Remi, like everyone else who worked in the quarry, had had to put up with verbal abuse on a daily basis from the boss-man but the idea that his parents had wanted to get rid of him was something the boss-man had not stooped to before and it was too much for Remi. The other boys fled frantically through the doorway but for some reason the boss-man's comment stopped Remi in his tracks.

"Liar! Liar!" he shouted, in the kind of loud, defiant tone that no boss-man could possibly afford to ignore. "They didn't want to get rid of me, they didn't!"

The boss-man's eyes homed in on Remi while his right hand reached for the well-worn compartment in his dungarees that harboured his dreaded cane. The other boys froze in disbelief, wondering what was going to happen and not knowing what to do for the best. They'd seen the cruelty of the boss-man many times before.

"You said I'd be well looked after, you said I'd be fed properly, you said that I'd have a nice bed to sleep in and you said that you'd send them money every week." His whole body spat out the words with the force of a volcanic eruption, past a heart that had never been called upon to beat so fast, driven by a boiling fury that refused to be contained any longer.

The boss-man looked incredulously at the small boy he towered over and after a few seconds began to laugh out loud. It wasn't so much what the boy was saying but the whole idea of such a puny wimp thinking that he could get one over on him!

'God, he's as stupid as his bloody parents,' he thought to himself, as his laughter turned to a violent, uncontrollable anger. "Come here you little bastard! I'll teach you to speak to me like that! You've gone too far this time!"

Before the words had passed his lips, he lashed out with his cane and, as Remi instinctively turned away, the blow caught him square across his naked back. He fell to the ground and as he did, he felt the fear that slaves, confronted by the reality of being the property of another human being, had felt all down the ages. Some kind of survival instinct brought him straight back to his feet, just out of reach of the boss-man's second blow.

He quickly realised that he needed to put as much distance as possible between himself and the boss-man's flailing cane and he made a dash for the open doorway. The other boys parted, keen to have nothing to do with either him or the boss-man. Remi made for the open ground at the base of the quarry. Suddenly, the boss-man's whistle rang out above the commotion, attracting the attention of two other cane-wielding supervisors.

Remi had nowhere to go. The quarry was securely fenced. The other boys were frozen with terror as the two supervisors and the boss-man closed in on him. It didn't take them long to capture him.

"Give him to me!" the boss-man said as he grabbed Remi from the firm grip of one of the supervisors. "I'm gonna teach this little bastard a lesson he won't forget."

The boss-man dragged Remi, kicking and screaming, to the centre of the compound. He was determined to make sure that every single boy in the quarry knew what would happen if they stepped out of line. He silenced Remi with one blow from the back of his hand and the young boy fell to the dusty floor once again. This time he didn't get up. He was badly dazed. Everything went quiet in his head. He could see the blows from the boss-man's cane raining in on him but for some reason he felt nothing. He could see everything clearly, the boss-man, the other boys, the quarry crane and the trucks beyond but then everything went dark.

Having exhausted himself, the boss-man stopped beating the small boy's limp body and there was only silence. The other boys didn't know if Remi was dead or alive. Remi knew—he was dead.

KIM TRUSTY

What you wish for

at first I hope for rescue
from the incessant quiet
that pounds my ears and
the frugal company of
parents who can't see
eye-to-eye

daughter of Medusa & Caliban
born under a waning moon and
pale as November
I grow amidst stealthy silence
and half languages
learning quickly that
a voice is of little use

apparently
one never tires
of dreaming escape
the debutante dress
spun of dry sea-weed
and fisherman's netting
the tanned hands of the pirate king
who takes you aboard
makes you queen

but you never really escape
from hair full of snakes
a smile with too many teeth
and a voice that alternates
between zephyr and hurricane's roar

beginning, middle, end?

I draw story arcs
for you and me
hope to read narrative thrusts
like tea leaves at the bottom
of an empty mug
because I don't know
where we're going
and I can't sit back and
enjoy the ride
because I'm not that kind
of girl your momma
told you to bring home
cream coloured slips
sensible shoes and
a handbag to match

naw
I'm tattoos and sexy hips
feminist thought action
and backseat fuckin'
my beginning middle and end
are never linear
will never be linear
and probably won't end
in happily ever after
because I'm not interested
in fairytales

I want reality
I want your reality
no matter how ugly

sons from other mothers
girls on the sly
older brothers locked inside
tell me
your stories
weave them with mine
create
tapestry
to cover the damp
on the wall
a rug
to hide the burn marks
a duvet
to keep our love warm
and hide it
from what can hurt

antique roadshow revisited

a jail hidden
behind the rotting wood
of a Kentucky tobacco farm
one stop in the
transcontinental network
of holding pens, jails & yards
a warehouse of human traffic

this slave ship
turned upside down
on the banks of the Ohio River
that fickle water, smelling of freedom

ADRIAN URMANOV

several short love affairs with the same woman at the
same time in amzei market

I

such a beautiful girl like you!
who would have thought that you're really so—
so horribly—
I'd never have thought!
somebody like yourself so young and so seemingly happy
to actually—
myself for example I look back
and I look forward
there's a better chance to recognise yourself looking back
and to stop yourself
don't turn that way don't mind this don't think that
dress warmer than you've actually done
of course you can stretch
also forwards—cut out stills of yourself
close-ups
multiply them in 2 or 3 hundred xerox copies

I'd never have thought!
somebody like yourself
so young and so seemingly happy
to actually—

I would love to spread them all over
bucharest on walls in the tram stations on the
335 and 336 bus routes all the way to the campus
you choose the actual places

I can help you lay the glue on the back side of the paper

I'd never have thought for one minute!
I'd never have got it—not in a thousand years
that you yourself
just like me—

II

why not?!
why not right now?

you can glue yourself on the walls in amzei market from
up there you can watch yourself freely observe how

it's still you walking between the stalls tasting the fruits

and you can choose
a new close-up-stick it on your t-shirt to find out who you're
actually embracing
or glue it on the interior side of the t-shirt and you'll see
how the skin rubs against the fabric

and the fine hair on your chest crushed between the shirt and
your breasts

I'm surprised you don't know
your own irritations—on your only real skin

you can practically walk for days
cutting out stills and hanging posters
                              stop behind each of them
                              and watch yourself
keep watching yourself—until you get
the real purpose of the sounds you let out

and the innumerable categories of movements of your eyeballs

                    you keep pointing to directions
                    you never start in
                    you surprise me I'm irritated even
                    by how many statements you make
                    and you never inhabit

the tip of a 1/3 inch long hour-hand on a wristwatch
travels at 0.00000275 mph.

I

                              I can't believe this
                    not for the life of me could I believe this
                              —laughing like an idiot
                    climbing on top of a tree and pretending
                              you hold its roots with you—
                              is it possible to be so demented
                              to believe to actually believe
                              if one climbs on top of a tree
                    he automatically becomes that tree's extension
                    I don't like at all the way you think

some   guy   was   thinking   just   like   you   and
let   me   tell   you   what   happened   to   him:

he lived in a small house on a thin· street
he moved perfectly negligently
no respect not the vaguest bother
for the milliards of organisms he demobilised daily
at every step
each time randomly placing his sole
in   unexpected   unannounced   locations—he   had
permanently stuck
death on his soles
and was stamping the streets without any concern
with the crassest lack of consideration
you're still laughing I can see that
you think I'm not paying attention—I know everything
actually I'm surprised you didn't vanish entirely
is this a suitable place to listen to something of such
importance?
is this the proper attitude? don't fool yourself
slowly
slowly it's going to happen
just like this—big and tough it's going to catch you
this stupid smile will freeze on your face
how tough are you when you comb your hair and
how virile are you watching your hair in the washbasin?
one ordinary day
all of them rebelled—all the days he'd turned to ashes
with his giving no fuck all the painful deaf noises that he'd
completely ignored
huge insects with terrible axes in their jaws
filled his mouth with tin and dust and whatever else they
found on the pavement

that morning
took him by force
and carried him far away to a place
I can't tell you about
                                and this only because
of the way you look somewhere else when I'm talking to you
and for the thoughts you fornicate with while I'm telling you
                                        everything
there in that place in that house
they threw him to the floor
tightly tied him up in steel or iron handcuffs
and while he was roaring grunting bellowing out of his nose
                                        because of
            the fiery pain
they crunched his soles
the insects with terrible axes in their jaws
                                why are you smiling?
                you're much stupider than I thought
                I almost don't give a damn anymore
        I'm doing these—warning you of all these just
                                        out of duty
they spat them—his soles—in small cotton bags
and hung them from the window for a few weeks to dry out
like chileans hung their mummies
—while cutting out pieces of him
the insects with terrible axes in their jaws
pieces of flesh dipped in adrenaline like sauce
and turning him on all sides
and randomly gluing back those fragments on him
                        where are you leaving? are you really this
                                                this
                actually you're not worth telling anything
                        you deserve it all—everything
that will—

II

I have to fix
  these dry fragments of soles into small cracks in the pavement
      in various parts of bucharest—and in these places
          if you sit in these places
              everything you say
                  clots
                      —happens

flower remains in warm milk

                    I

she shakes her hands and her fingers grow into long needles of
      stainless metal which she sticks into everybody coming
      / in her way there are trees / and her fingers pointed to
      the sky are trees and her teeth pointed to the sky are
      trees and the strands of hair trees
they grow downwards screw into the ground get through the
      ground and exit on the other side and there
they point to the sky and
they are stainless trees

II

and she says I love you / eyes white as foam / you feel like
     licking her eyes suck them out of her head with their
     roots and
eyes drag after them the core of the brain and
love cleans everything
even the brain the fertilizer of her eyes and hair and then I
     lick the white of her eyes and
love cleans everything
and I suck her eye-liquid and brain and then the roots of the
     hair and the strands of hair from the ground leave
     the sky through the centre of the earth
through her head
stainless trees—I suck at once with the whipped milk on her
     retinas / she and her arms / lick her arms with fear in
     your mouth / her arms like icicles and she's
     shrinking getting smaller and smaller more and
     more fragile until you get to her fingers and her nails
love cleans everything
reabsorb in my flesh stainless needles threatening trees
     pointing to the sky but me
poor me
I munch them me miserable me I whisper I
love you

III

and she melts away / more and more absent-minded
aimless
and she gets absorbed
entirely
from the core of her head to the nails—her guts out like a

cloth I'm left to hold in my arms and me
poor me miserable me
tonight there will be silence again whispers again

IV

I lay her on the bed / cover the mattress with her
I lay her like a bed-linen I lie down and wait to fall asleep me
        poor me miserable me I don't brush my teeth I've got
        bits of her between my teeth
how can I touch the teeth
I wait an hour I wait many hours and I know behind the
        walls other couples wait for nothing
other couples have the night in front of them like a glass of
        warm milk

V

a glass of warm milk that you wait for
the entire day and you drink it with great joy—before falling
        asleep or even in the middle of the night when you
        know others also
in that silence
but you must never talk about how others—
this mustn't leave the hole in your stomach where you are
        allowed to talk about this
you can describe sip by sip how this happens
—and then you can drink in the morning your eyes still
        closed you can drink slowly as if someone's just
        offered you a flower and you smell it without lifting
        your eyes and you know you'll blush

but you postpone or
−you can let yourself be drunk leisurely sipped however the
    other wants to / from far away from the sleep still
no need to actually get involved

VI

but me poor me miserable me I lie over you and lick my teeth
    gather you from my molars still cold pieces still of a
    different temperature from that of my mouth
love cleans everything and I wait an hour I wait many hours
    with still foreign pieces in my mouth I lie down and
    suddenly understand indeed love
love cleans everything love cleans even love

VII

I pull you over me and try to cover myself completely like
mom o mom covered me when it was dark and she brought
    me a glass of warm milk sweetened with honey and
    she lay next to me whispered things
things she whispered and wrapped me up from head to toe
    like a pancake like a mummy like mom's doll and air
    gradually reached the temperature of my body and
then I knew that suddenly outside the blanket it turned very
    very cold

VIII

that's how I pull you over me−like mom wrapped me into
    mom's doll you're already stiff at margins and this
    frightens me makes me hurry−cover seal myself
and air reaches the temperature of my body and you're hard

as tin by now and the last pieces between my
        teeth are warmer almost warm
warm as my mouth
//
and everything grows mouldy—with warmth / beautifully /
        in this embalming scent and me
poor me
miserable me I'm clean because love cleans everything love
        cleans
even love.

IVÁN DARIO VARGAS RONCANCIO

Cementerio de gotas

Hoy, estuve cultivando tristezas.
Las gotas de agua pegaban impunemente sobre algunos
hombros,
y las húmedas aceras eras espejos olvidados,
por los que transitaban cuerpos encogidos, hacia los
habitáculos de siempre.
Mientras cultivava mis tristezas bajo la lluvia
la ciudad me rechazaba.
Hoy, ella quería estar a solas con su nombre,
quería limpiarse la humanidad de encima.
Yo tuíe transgresor, el voyeur, el husmeador.
¿De que hablan los paredes?
¿De que hablan con sus sombras?
Ya no hay más palabras que callen el sonido del aire,
entre los espacios delgados de la edificios.
Ya no hay más pasos que ignores sus huellas invisibles
ni más respiros que le roben el aire al aire.
La ciudad destizo nuestros ruidos
y el recuerdo de unos zapatos blancos se estampa en mi
mente,
mientras mis manos empuñan el vacío.
Me reflejo en las vitrinas y en otras superficies,
y mi rostro, sobre la acera húmeda,
como una chispa amarilla de óleo sobre un papel
delgado.

A esta hora, la ciudad es apenas un cementerio de gotas:
esos pegueños cuerpas persistentes.

114

Raindrop Cemetery

Today, I was cultivating sadness,
the drops of water hitting unpunishingly against
shoulders
and the wet pavements forgotten mirrors
across which hunched bodies proceeded towards the
colonies of forever.
Cultivating my sadness under rain, I felt
that the city rejected me.
Today, she wanted to be alone with her name,
she wanted to clean humanity from her sides.
I was the transgressor, the voyeur.
Of what do the walls speak?
Of what do they speak with their shadows?
There are no more words silencing the air's sound
between the thin spaces of the buildings.
There are no more footsteps ignoring their invisible
prints
nor breaths stealing air from the air.
The city unmade all our noises
and the memory of one pair of white shoes stamps itself
into my mind
while my hands seize the emptiness.
I am reflected in the plate-glass and in other surfaces
and my face on wet pavements is like a spark of yellow
oil against thin paper.

At this time, the city is a cemetery of drops barely:
little persistent bodies.

Dejó de ser un monstruo de órganos muertos.
Se convirtió en instante. Y yo lo vivo en ella.
Me dejé invadir de sus silencios que alimentaron mis
tristezas.

La ciudad me atrapaba.
Cada boca calle, tendía redes invisibles de aliento
enuejecido que envolvían mi cuerpo.
Primero, me sacó los ojos: deambulaba a tientas por sus
calles.
Luego, me cortó los lorazos: ahora mi cuerpo pegaba
contra las paredes.
Me cortó las piernas, de ese modo me quitoel camino.
Sin mirada, sin tacto, sin camino, me convirtió en
escultura,
parqueada a la orilla del abismo de cualquier acera.

She was allowed to be a monster, composed of dead
organs.
She changed in an instant. And I'm living it,
Her confidences feeding my sadness.

The city trapped me.
Each street-opening spreads invisible nets of aged breath
which have surrounded my body.
First she plucked out my eyes. I wandered blind through
her streets.
Then, she cut off my arms. Now my body hits against the
walls.
She cut off my legs. Without vision, without touch,
without path
she converted me into a sculpture, parked on the brink
of any pavement's abyss.

Appendix
(Local media representations)

GIPSY CLEAN-UP BILL RUNS INTO THOUSANDS [1]
Taxpayers face increasing cost
By Samantha Nanda

Coventry taxpayers are facing a hefty bill for the cat-and-mouse game gipsies [sic] are playing across the city.

The clean-up costs alone have shot up to £7,5000 and the legal bill is adding many thousands more.

The travellers have now moved on to the fifth site since April, leaving a trail of court orders, upset residents and litter.

The same 'family'—made up of about 17 caravans and motor vehicles—have moved off sites as legal proceedings got under way.

Reports of aggressive behaviour, rubbish dumped on green land and even excrement and nappies being left behind have upset people living near the sites.

The council has officers negotiating with the travellers who have indicated they will leave their current site at Coundon Hall Park, near Waste Lane, on Sunday.

Mick Green, head of public protection in the city services directorate, said the council is doing what it can to resolve the problems.

He said that each time the gipsies moved to a site the council must, by law, send in officers to look at their welfare and health needs before beginning proceedings.

This usually happens on the day the camp is reported, then a court order is sought to remove them from the land which can take between seven and 10 days as court time needs to be found and documentation prepared.

Mr Green stressed that in 90 per cent of cases the travelers move on within the time given as they know the law very well.

He explained: "This is a process we have to go through every time by law. We can't obtain a blanket order to restrict them from moving anywhere within the city, by law."

He said the council cleaned up as soon as possible after travellers left.

Each clean up costs between £1,000 and £1,500. The council also provides them with the skips.

Mr Green added: "These people may have a different style of life but they have the same rights as everyone else. We operate as quickly and as best we can within the constraints of the law to deal with the issue."

He said gipsies were here because they could make money, and people should help by saying no to doorstep sellers.

The gipsies' travels have been:

April 15—on to private land in Kingswood Close, Holbrooks.

April 28—moved on to part-private and part-council land in Newport Road, Holbrooks.

May 12—moved on to Sowe Common, off Woodway Lane, Walsgrave.

May 22—moved on to recreation land off Humber Road, Stoke.

May 23—moved on to Coundon Hall Park, near Waste Lane, Keresley.

*

We, the undersigned, condemn unreservedly the story 'Gipsy bill runs into thousands' that appeared on the front page of The Coventry Evening Telegraph on Friday 28th May.

We deplore its publication on the following grounds:

1. The use of the term "gipsies" [lower case g] is both insulting ⅄ and inaccurate: do the people belong to the Roma Nation or to a particular ethnic group (Romani, Sinti, etc)?

2. The opening paragraph ("Coventry taxpayers are facing a hefty bill for the cat-and-mouse game gipsies are playing across the city.") contains heavy bias (Coventry is depicted as the 'mouse' to these people's malevolent 'cat') which is not countered either here or later in the article. Why is the possibility not considered that the Council are victimising the travellers by moving them from site to site, that the 'cat-and-mouse game' is in fact being played by the city's representatives against powerless people within their jurisdiction?

3. The costs of removing the travellers' litter are not compared to any other figures (ie. the cost of removing litter from an established housing estate of equivalent size, or, the normal cost of removal from the parks in question). This lack of a 'control' measurement calls into serious doubt the relevance of the figures quoted and, by extension, the entire article, whose ostensible purpose is to bring these figures to the public.

4. There is no coverage of the problem's root causes (for example, the well-documented cases of ethnic persecution of travellers in Eastern European states), which could provide an intellectually objective counterbalance to the claim that "What we must remember is that they are here in Coventry because there is money to be made." This view, expressed by the 'head of public protection in the city services directorate', is the only one quoted in the article. Similarly, no alternatives to his claim that "We operate as quickly and as best we can within the constraints of the law to deal with the issue" are given, for example by exploring the idea that there are other options to the 'moving on' of travellers,

such as the creation of an enclave where they can stay.

5. The overall picture to be drawn of travellers from the article is that they are messy ("Reports of aggressive behaviour, dumping rubbish on green land and even excrement and nappies being left on sites have upset people living near the areas"), expensive and conniving ("Mr Green stressed that in 90 per cent of cases the travellers move on within the time given as they know the law very well"). However, for the reasons outlined in Points 3 and 4 above, this inference is not drawn from any facts, but relies instead for its legitimacy on hostile assumptions as to what their lifestyle consists of. This risks discriminating against the travellers on the ground of race. [3]

6. The article contains overt similarities with the stated policies of the far-right British National Party, [4] a dangerously partial stance for a newspaper to take in the run-up to an election.

7. The article's timing (published on the Friday before a Bank Holiday weekend and thirteen days before local elections where the BNP are fielding a candidate) has been designed to maximise its political impact and reduce the amount of dissent that could reasonably be expected from readers.

8. The Coventry Evening Telegraph has for the reasons above allowed its standards to slip and can justly be accused of shoddy journalism (partial, uncritical and inflammatory) and sensationalist editing (this 'story' was given the entire front page).

We therefore call on the writer of the article and the newspaper's editor to withdraw the article in full, and to apologise publicly to the travellers who are its subject. [5]

Wes Webb
Chief Executive, Coventry Refugee Centre

Penny Walker
Coventry Peace House

Deepak Naik
Minorities of Europe

Colin Bell
Coventry Black Arts Forum

Frances Porter
Frontline AV

George Ttoouli
The Heaventree Press

Vibert Cornwall
Chair, Coventry West Indian Association

David Morley
University of Warwick

Margery Jones
Coventry Against Racism

NOTES

[1] Front page story in The Coventry Evening Telegraph on Friday 28th May, 2004.

[2] "Capitalize names of linguistic, tribal, religious, and other groups. Lower-case designations based on color, size, or local usage. Examples: black, white, Latina, Hispanic, American Indian, redneck, Alaska Natives, Euro-American, Jew, Mesoamerican, highlander, Indo-European, Native Americans, Pacific Islander, mestizo. African American (n, adj; cap, no hyphen). Cap Australian Aboriginal and Aborigine, but lower-case aboriginal otherwise." — from the 'Style Guide' of the American Anthropological Association, http://www.swt.edu/~rw04/anthropology/info/theory/long-style-guide.htm.

[3] See 'Discrimination against Gypsies and Travellers is the last 'respectable' form of racism, says the CRE', Commission for Racial Equality news release, http:www.cre.gov.uk/media/nr_arch/2004/nr040402.html (2nd April 2004).

[4] "On May 1st, around one million East European gypsies get the right to flood into Britain and live at our expense or undercut our wages..." — 'E.U. Gypsy Flood', front page article from the BNP's Freedom From The EU (undated) newsletter distributed in Tile Hill in late May and early June.

[5] Presented to The Coventry Evening Telegraph on Thursday 3rd June 2004, for the editor's attention. We still await a formal response from the newspaper.